WRITING EXTRAVAGANZA!

Writing EXTRAVAGANZA!

Journal Prompts & Story Starters for Creative Kids

5th Grade Edition

The Playhard Press

Asheville Bellingham Ithaca

Writing Extravaganza!
Journal Prompts and Story Starters for Creative Kids, 5th Grade Ed.
Third Edition

Copyright © 2020, 2022 by The Playhard Project

Published by The Playhard Press
The Playhard Press is an imprint of The Playhard Project LLC.

Matthew Barrington, Managing Director
Margaret Ellis, Series Editor
Abdul MuQeet, Graphic Design
Steven B. Dodson, Operations Consultant
Chelsea Cooper, Strategy Consultant

playhardpress.com
playhardproject.com
writingextravaganza.com

ISBN 978-1-954305-08-3

Dedication

To Mrs. Charny

PJ, Ricky, Louie, Steven, Tim, Mikey

and 12th Street

Whether the weather is cold
Or whether the weather is hot
Whatever the weather, we're in this together
Whether we like it or not!

Welcome!

To the greatest writing book ever!

What is a Writing Extravaganza anyway?

It's like a circus with a bunch of different acts all under the same big tent. Variety is the spice of life—and this book is super spicy! There are oodles of different prompts to easily get your creative sparks flying.

What's inside?

There are story starters that are taken from the actual lives of real kids. There are prompts that explore the best of times and the worst of times, the opposites found in life, and a little bit of everything in between. Some prompts daydream about if you could do something, while others get real because you know you can't. There are poetry challenges, true crime stories, ideas to get to the bottom of problems, and different ways to think about stuff, too. There are letters to yourself in the future and the past, pages to drain your brain, tons of deep thoughts, and much, much more!

How does it work?

There is no wrong way to use this book! Flip through and find something that speaks to you, then go for it! Don't hold back—this book is for you to get it all out! You can write *anything* you want, *anywhere* you want, *anytime* you want, about *anybody* you want, *anyway* you want! There are no rules: Just write! And write! And write! And write! And write! And write!

Sometimes my friends want to play Daredevil. They stand on the crossbar of their bikes, hold on to the handlebars, and ride down a big hill. I felt like if I didn't do it too, they would make fun of me. Also, I wanted them to like me. We were at the top of the hill with our bikes and...

_____

_____

_____

_____

_____

_____

_____

_____

_____

_____

_____

_____

_____

_____

If I Could Go Back...

If I could go back and do-over a really bad day, I would! Here's what happened on that day...

_____

_____

_____

_____

_____

_____

_____

_____

_____

_____

_____

_____

_____

_____

The biggest things I regret about this day are:

_____   _____

_____   _____

But I Can't!

But I can't go back and change the past. I can only change the future! Here's how I'm going to choose to live from now on...

_____

_____

_____

_____

_____

_____

_____

_____

_____

These are some mistakes that I want to make sure I don't repeat in the future:

_____

_____

_____

Past Changes

These are some big changes that have already happened in my life in the past...

_____

_____

_____

_____

_____

_____

Sometimes we don't realize all the changes we've gone through! How have some of these changes made you a stronger kid and more able to bounce back?

_____

_____

_____

_____

_____

Changes Ahead

Here are a bunch of changes that are going to happen
in my life in the future...

_____

_____

_____

_____

_____

_____

_____

Ever stop to think that you've made it through 100% of
all your bad days? How can all the changes that you've
overcome give you confidence for the changes ahead?

_____

_____

_____

_____

_____

_____

The kid with long hair said he wanted to fight Binny. He got on our bus after school and followed us to our bus stop. We got off with Binny and some kids called out, "Fight, fight, fight!" Binny was scared and...

_____

_____

_____

_____

_____

_____

_____

_____

_____

_____

_____

_____

_____

_____

_____

Upside Down

Write about different times when your life has been
turned totally upside down...

_____

_____

_____

_____

_____

_____

_____

_____

How were you able to get your life right-side up again?
What advice would you give to a friend?

_____

_____

_____

_____

Right-Side Up

Keeping your life from turning upside down is hard sometimes! Think of some helpful things you already do to stay feeling right-side up...

_____

_____

_____

Below are activities that keep kids feeling balanced. Put down the things you do and how often for each—

Exercise: _____

_____

Sleep: _____

_____

Nutrition: _____

_____

Self-Care: _____ *Self-Care List in the back of the book!*

_____

Recreation: _____

_____

My own ideas: _____

_____

A Letter to

Write a letter to your future self. Do you have any advice you want to tell future you? What are all the things you want to remember? Remind yourself about what is most important.

_____

_____

_____

_____

_____

_____

_____

_____

_____

_____

_____

_____

_____

_____

_____

the Future

_____

_____

_____

_____

_____

_____

_____

_____

_____

_____

_____

_____

_____

_____

_____

_____

_____

_____

_____

Our teacher is in the hospital and can't come to school for the rest of the year. We got a new teacher named Mrs. Gonda. She looks old and mean and I think she hates kids. How are we going to survive? On her very first day, she...

_____

_____

_____

_____

_____

_____

_____

_____

_____

_____

_____

_____

_____

_____

If I Could Go...

If I could go to a movie and hold hands with anyone from school, here's who I would choose and how I imagine our special night together...

_____

_____

_____

_____

_____

_____

_____

_____

_____

_____

_____

_____

_____

_____

_____

_____

_____

_____

_____

_____

_____

But I Can't!

But I can't hold hands at a movie with anyone I want. There are some ways I can show people how I feel and what I think about them, like...

_____

_____

_____

_____

Would you want someone to be honest with you about their feelings? It takes courage to tell someone how you feel. Would you have more self-respect if you did?

_____

_____

_____

_____

_____

Rejection happens to everyone sometimes. What can you do if someone doesn't like you back?

_____

_____

_____

_____

Hold On

Write about all the good things that you want to hold on to or bring into your life...

_____

_____

_____

_____

_____

_____

_____

_____

Knowing what we want in our life is important. It can be hard work to hold on to those things sometimes. What can you do to keep the good things in your life?

_____

_____

_____

_____

_____

_____

Let Go

Unpack all the bad things in your life that you want to let go of for good...

_____

_____

_____

_____

_____

_____

_____

_____

Knowing how we want things to be different is also important. Now that you have a list, what can you do to start letting these things go?

_____

_____

_____

_____

_____

_____

During reading class, a boy was breaking a pink eraser into little bits. Then, he used a plastic spoon like a catapult to shoot the little bits across the room at people when the teacher wasn't looking. He thought it was funny, but then...

_____

_____

_____

_____

_____

_____

_____

_____

_____

_____

_____

_____

_____

The Best

The best things about being my gender are...

_____

_____

_____

_____

_____

_____

_____

_____

Are some of the things that you like about your gender privileges that other people don't have? What kind of hardships do other genders face that you do not?

_____

_____

_____

_____

_____

The Worst

The worst things about being my gender are...

_____

_____

_____

_____

What are some ideas about gender that you think are
old-fashioned or unfair?

_____

_____

_____

_____

Have you seen people treated differently because of
their gender? How do you think they felt?

_____

_____

_____

_____

Fitting In

These are the things I do to fit in...

_____

_____

_____

_____

_____

_____

Describe some times in your life when you felt like you
really fit in...

_____

_____

_____

_____

_____

_____

_____

_____

Standing Out

Here are the things I do to stand out...

_____

_____

_____

_____

_____

_____

Write about some times when you really stood out
from the crowd...

_____

_____

_____

_____

_____

_____

_____

_____

_____

My parent signed me up for this thing called Cotillion. It's where boys and girls get dressed up in ties and dresses and learn how to ballroom dance. Luckily for me, two of my friends were also signed up. We went to the first class feeling nervous, embarrassed, and uncomfortable in our formal clothes. There were tons of kids there! Some were from our school. The instructors made us get quiet. Then, they ordered us to find our first dance partner...

_____

_____

_____

_____

_____

_____

_____

_____

_____

_____

_____

Brain on Autopilot?

When something bad happens, the first thought that pops into our mind is usually negative. Thanks a lot, brain! 😠 What are some negative things your brain might say to you in the following situations:

You make a poor grade on a test.

Negative
Thought ➡
_____

A friend invites someone else over, not you.

Negative
Thought ➡
_____

The teacher embarrasses you in front of the class.

Negative
Thought ➡
_____

You get made fun of because of _____ .

Fill in the Blank

Negative
Thought ➡
_____

You get caught doing something wrong.

Negative
Thought ➡
_____

The person you like doesn't like you.

Negative
Thought ➡
_____

Do you know the worst part about thinking these things? They're not even true! It's just our brain on autopilot, saying negative stuff. But when we hear these things in our head, guess what? It makes us feel bad about ourselves. And who wants that?

Nope, I'm the Pilot!

You are the pilot that gets to steer your brain—not the other way around. Changing those autopilot thoughts can change how you feel overall. Let's take the same situations and write a better thought to replace it:

Okay, so I made a bad grade on a test...

A Better Thought ⟹ _____

So my friend invited someone else over this time...

A Better Thought ⟹ _____

I got embarrassed in front of everyone, but...

A Better Thought ⟹ _____

Just because they made fun of me...

A Better Thought ⟹ _____

Okay, I got caught doing something I shouldn't...

A Better Thought ⟹ _____

The person I like doesn't like me the same way...

A Better Thought ⟹ _____

Now you know that negative thoughts are what pop up first—and you know that they're not really true! The game is to catch them, stop them, and change them to something that serves you better. This little action boosts our self-esteem in a huge way. Try it!

My Imagination

Let's use the power of our imagination to create a relaxing, peaceful scene. You know how your heart speeds up when you're watching an action movie? Your brain knows it's not real, but your body still has a reaction! In the same way, we can trick our brains into doing just the opposite—by imagining a relaxing place, our bodies can feel like we're actually there! The secret is to use all five of your senses.

First, choose the most relaxing place in the world that you can possibly imagine:

_____

Next, list everything about your place that you can sense— really dive in and describe all the little details!

I can see: _____

_____

I can hear: _____

_____

I can feel: _____

_____

I can smell: _____

_____

I can taste: _____

_____

Mini Vacation

Last, put yourself in the scene. Where are you and what are you doing? Use all those sensory details to paint the most vivid picture you can! The more detailed you make it, the more you can trick your mind into thinking you're actually there—and the more relaxed and better you'll feel!

_____

_____

_____

_____

_____

_____

_____

_____

_____

_____

_____

_____

Now that you created this vivid, calming scene—close your eyes and imagine you are there! Return to this special place to take a mini vacation whenever you need a break from your busy life. The more you practice this, the easier it becomes!

In a special class, we were allowed to take apart old machines. There was a blender, a toaster, a vacuum, a computer, and a bunch of other things, too. We had to take everything apart and then put the pieces back together to make something new. We invented something amazing! We called it...

_____

_____

_____

_____

_____

_____

_____

_____

_____

_____

_____

_____

_____

My Family's Best

The best things about my family are...

_____

_____

_____

_____

_____

_____

_____

_____

Describe the ways that you add to the good things you like about your family...

_____

_____

_____

_____

_____

_____

My Family's Worst

The worst things about my family are...

_____

_____

_____

_____

_____

_____

Think about ways you could do your part to improve some things you don't like about your family...

_____

_____

_____

_____

_____

Of all the things you wrote, which one is the easiest to do? Could it make a difference? Would it hurt to try?

_____

_____

Lies I Have Told

These are some lies I have told other people...

_____

_____

_____

_____

_____

Sometimes people carry around feelings of guilt or
shame that haunt them like a ghost. If you feel bad
about something—it's never too late to repair the
damage. You could always apologize and do
something nice for the people that were hurt like:

_____

_____

_____

_____

_____

Can you promise yourself that you won't repeat the
same mistakes in the future? If you can start to accept
what happened, the ghost of regret will be free to go.

Lies Told to Me

Here are the lies that other people have told me...

_____

_____

_____

_____

_____

When we're lied to, we get angry. But anger doesn't ride alone! Other feelings are hidden beneath our anger. For example, if we feel hurt? We get angry! Feel jealous? Angry! Feel let down? Again—angry! Think about these lies or times you've been angry recently— can you find which other emotions were behind it?

_____

_____

_____

_____

_____

_____

Feeling & Emotion Vocabulary Wheel in the back of the book!

I'm having a rough time with my Valentine's Day cards. I tried to get a head start, but now Valentine's Day is almost here! I don't know what to write on some of them. It's kinda complicated. You see...

_____

_____

_____

_____

_____

_____

_____

_____

_____

_____

_____

_____

_____

_____

If I Could Fly Away...

If I could grow wings and fly far away from this place,
I would...

_____

_____

_____

_____

_____

_____

_____

_____

_____

_____

_____

Here are some things I wish I could escape:

_____   _____

_____   _____

But I Can't!

But I can't just fly away. I can talk about the stuff that makes me feel like flying away sometimes, like...

_____

_____

_____

_____

_____

_____

_____

_____

Sometimes life is hard to accept. But things are the way they are. Refusing to accept stuff in your life doesn't change anything. It can actually add to painful feelings. What things do you have trouble accepting?

_____

_____

_____

_____

Write a wonderful
adventure about this
mermaid and her lovely
turtle named Jimbo...

_____

_____

_____

_____

_____

_____

_____

_____

_____

_____

_____

_____

_____

_____

_____

_____

Today after school I will play my first game of basketball on the team. I'm supposed to wear a blue shirt and white shorts. We must win this to be in the 5th Grade Championship. The other team wants to win, too. They have a secret weapon. Their name is...

_____

_____

_____

_____

_____

_____

_____

_____

_____

_____

_____

_____

_____

_____

Writing My

The one, the only—the story of your life! As told by the author themselves, this dramatic retelling is taking the world by storm. Give your unique perspective on the major events of your life. How has your life unfolded? Do you dare to write about your life in the future? Start with a great title and tell your story to the world!

_____

_____

_____

_____

_____

_____

_____

_____

_____

_____

_____

_____

Autobiography

Really Lonely

These are some times when I felt really lonely...

_____

_____

_____

_____

The next time I start to feel this way, I can plan to...

Talk to these people: _____

_____

_____

Listen to my favorite music: _____

_____

_____

Distract myself with these activities: _____

_____ *Distraction List in the back of the book!*

_____

Tell myself these positive things: _____

_____

_____

My own ideas: _____

Really Loved

Here are some other times when I felt really loved...

_____

_____

_____

_____

_____

The time is always right to tell people that you're glad
they're in your life. Here are ways I can show others
how much I appreciate their friendship and love:

_____

_____

_____

_____

_____

_____

_____

_____

_____

We were playing around in Eli's garage because it was raining outside. There was a worn out cardboard box that we found hidden in the junk. We opened it and there was an old, musty blanket on top. We couldn't believe it, but tucked under the blanket we found...

_____

_____

_____

_____

_____

_____

_____

_____

_____

_____

_____

_____

_____

_____

If I Could Have...

If I could have any job in the world that I can imagine
when I'm grown up, here's what I would choose and
how awesome it would be...

_____

_____

_____

_____

_____

_____

_____

_____

_____

_____

_____

_____

_____

_____

_____

_____

_____

_____

_____

_____

But I Can't!

But I can't have any job in the whole wide world. Here are some jobs that the grown-ups around me have and which ones I think I might be really good at...

_____

_____

_____

_____

_____

_____

_____

What happens to kids who don't really think about what they want to be when they're adults? Is it ever too soon to work toward a dream or career?

_____

_____

_____

_____

_____

Problem?

Describe a problem you are facing in detail:

_____

_____

_____

_____

_____

_____

_____

First, write down *three possible choices* to deal with the problem. Then, list all the advantages and the disadvantages of each choice.

Choice #1: _____

_____

Advantages of #1	Disadvantages of #1
_____	_____
_____	_____
_____	_____
_____	_____

Solution!

Choice #2: _____

_____

Advantages of #2	Disadvantages of #2
_____	_____
_____	_____
_____	_____
_____	_____

Choice #3: _____

_____

Advantages of #3	Disadvantages of #3
_____	_____
_____	_____
_____	_____
_____	_____

What does your heart tell you to do? _____

What does your brain tell you to do? _____

The best solution to the problem is: _____

It was the first day of class. Savannah was the first one in the classroom. She picked the first desk in the first row. She put her big box of crayons on the desk to claim it as hers and skipped out to her locker. When she came back, other kids were there. One kid was in her chair, looking at her crayons. Savannah went up to him and said...

_____

_____

_____

_____

_____

_____

_____

_____

_____

_____

_____

_____

The Best of Me

The best things about who I am are...

_____

_____

_____

_____

_____

_____

_____

How did you come to believe all of these great things?
Describe times when people complimented you or told
you these nice things about yourself:

_____

_____

_____

_____

_____

_____

_____

The Worst of Me

The worst things about myself are maybe...

_____

_____

_____

How we think that other people view us—changes our view of ourselves. But is what we imagine that they think even really true? Or do we make it up in our heads sometimes?

_____

_____

_____

Is it fair to use other people's judgements to measure our worth? I mean, who are they to say, anyway? Whose opinions matter to you the most?

_____

_____

_____

Worried

Describe all the things you feel worried about...

_____

_____

_____

_____

_____

_____

Our mind spends a lot of time stuck in a rut—thinking about the past or worrying about the future. How often does your brain "time travel" back and forth like this?

_____

_____

_____

_____

Make it a game to catch your brain when it does this! You can say, "Brain—STOP!" Then, come back to the present moment. Say, "No time travelling!" and focus all your attention on whatever it is that you're doing. Playing this game over and over will train your brain. Worries about the past or the future will start to fade. Right now is a gift, that's why we call it the present!

Confident

Jot down all the things you feel confident about...

_____

_____

_____

_____

_____

_____

_____

_____

_____

Did you always feel so confident about these things?
What advice would you tell a friend to help them build
up their confidence and self-esteem?

_____

_____

_____

_____

_____

At our sleepovers, the first person to fall asleep always gets a prank played on them. This time, the person to fall asleep first was me! My friends...

_____

_____

_____

_____

_____

_____

_____

_____

_____

_____

_____

_____

_____

_____

_____

The Letter

Write a letter that will never be sent. Say all the things you want to say to someone—but can't! Be honest. Get all of your feelings off your chest. Release your bottled up emotions and put them down on the page.

_____

_____

_____

_____

_____

_____

_____

_____

_____

_____

_____

_____

_____

to No One

_____

_____

_____

_____

_____

_____

_____

_____

_____

_____

_____

_____

_____

_____

_____

_____

_____

_____

_____

_____

_____

Warning! Do not give this letter to anyone, no matter how much you think you want to. This is for you, not for them! Don't do it!

Video games are fun to play sometimes. But I know a neighbor kid who played so much, they were all he ever thought about. Then one day, he actually believed that he got sucked into the game itself! He...

_____

_____

_____

_____

_____

_____

_____

_____

_____

_____

_____

_____

_____

_____

The Best Outcome

The best possible outcomes that could happen with a big problem I have are...

_____

_____

_____

_____

_____

_____

_____

_____

_____

Okay, if the best thing you can think of actually ended up happening—would you be good with that? Is it worth trying to fix a problem in order to get an outcome that's totally awesome and rewarding?

_____

_____

_____

_____

The Worst Outcome

The worst possible outcomes I can imagine with this same problem are...

_____

_____

_____

_____

_____

_____

_____

_____

_____

Now, if the worst of the worst happened, would you be able to get through it? Would you still be okay?

_____

If the worst happened, how would it affect your life:

In one week? _____

In one month? _____

In one year? _____

Heroes

Write all the things that you like about your heroes...

_____

_____

_____

_____

_____

_____

_____

_____

_____

What are some small things that you can do to be
more like the heroes you admire?

_____

_____

_____

_____

_____

Enemies

Describe the things you dislike about all the bad people in this crazy world...

_____

_____

_____

_____

_____

How can feelings of dislike help people to do good things? How could the things you don't like inspire you to make things just a little bit better in the world?

_____

_____

_____

_____

_____

_____

_____

_____

At recess, the boys were playing football again. All of a sudden, there was a bunch of yelling. I saw the heavy kid sitting on top of someone's head—on purpose. He was laughing. The kid under them was crying, yelling, and couldn't get up. I...

_____

_____

_____

_____

_____

_____

_____

_____

_____

_____

_____

_____

_____

_____

If I Could Live...

If I could live anywhere in the world, at any time in history—here's where I would choose and all the amazing things about it...

_____

_____

_____

_____

_____

_____

_____

_____

_____

_____

_____

_____

_____

_____

_____

_____

But I Can't!

But I can't change where I live. Here's where I live now and all the things I like and maybe sometimes don't like about living here…

_____

_____

_____

_____

_____

_____

_____

_____

_____

_____

_____

_____

_____

_____

_____

Poet's Choice

Write a love poem about your favorite food:

_____

_____

_____

_____

_____

_____

_____

_____

_____

_____

_____

_____

_____

_____

_____

_____

Poet's Challenge

The Couplet

When the last word of one line rhymes with the last word of the next line, they sound great together! They like each other so much, they are like a couple. Maybe that's why we call them a couplet! Try to write a poem made up of couplets like this:

Words can rhyme
Just take the time!

It's not hard
To be a bard!

I'm a cool poet
Now you know it!

_____

_____

_____

_____

_____

_____

_____

_____

_____

_____

_____

I told my friend a secret. They promised not to tell. But the next day, they told Jack and he's a loud mouth. Here's what happened. I told my friend...

_____

_____

_____

_____

_____

_____

_____

_____

_____

_____

_____

_____

_____

_____

_____

_____

Full Head?

The thoughts in your brain flow like a river or stream. This is a game to empty those thoughts from your head and let them flow onto the paper. Here's how to play—write every thought you have on these pages. Anything that comes to mind! No stopping. No thinking about what you're writing. Forget about spelling and mess ups—just keep going. Your hand starts to hurt? Keep going! You think it sounds stupid? Write that down and keep going! Whatever you do, don't stop writing the real-time thoughts, feelings, and comments your brain is making. Think you can make it to the bottom of the next page?

Ready? Get set—Flow!

_____

_____

_____

_____

_____

_____

_____

_____

_____

_____

_____

Brain Drain!

_____

_____

_____

_____

_____

_____

_____

_____

_____

_____

_____

_____

_____

_____

_____

_____

_____

_____

_____

Stop! Now ask yourself—how do I feel? This is a great way to release all the stuff that you didn't even know was weighing you down. Try it anytime your head feels too full or too busy!

Waste a Life

Write about how a person can waste their life...

_____

_____

_____

_____

_____

_____

_____

_____

_____

_____

_____

What are some negative beliefs that would lead a
person astray, to live an empty or meaningless life?

_____   _____   _____

_____   _____   _____

_____   _____   _____

Live a Good Life

Share how a person can live their life to the fullest...

_____

_____

_____

_____

_____

_____

_____

_____

_____

_____

What are some core values or beliefs that would guide
a person to live a rich, fulfilling life?

_____	_____	_____
_____	_____	_____
_____	_____	_____
_____	_____	_____
_____	_____	

*Core Values List
in the back of
the book!*

My favorite holiday is coming up. This year, I want to do something extra special. I can imagine...

_____

_____

_____

_____

_____

_____

_____

_____

_____

_____

_____

_____

_____

_____

_____

_____

The Way Things Are

Just because things are the way they are right now—doesn't mean they'll always be that way. Write about all the things you're not satisfied with in your life.

_____

_____

_____

_____

_____

_____

_____

_____

Accepting that "things are the way they are" can help with feeling frustrated. This is easy if you take a deep breath and remind yourself that things won't last forever. Is this true for some of the stuff you wrote?

_____

_____

_____

The Way They Will Be

People are always growing and changing. That's the great thing about being human! Often, characters in stories start out one way. Then, they face challenges, learn about themselves, and grow. By the end, they're a different person. Write about your challenges, what you will learn, and the person you will grow to be.

_____

_____

_____

_____

_____

_____

_____

_____

_____

_____

_____

_____

_____

Family

Your family is here to help you. But they won't know
you have a problem unless you tell them about it.
Sometimes your family knows about a problem, but
doesn't know how they can help. If you want help
from others, you also have to show that you are trying
to help yourself. Use this template to present a
problem to your family, explain how they can help
you, and how you are trying to help yourself.

My biggest problem: _____

_____

_____

_____

How others can help me: How I can help myself:

_____   _____

_____   _____

_____   _____

_____   _____

_____   _____

_____   _____

Matters

A medium problem: _____

_____

_____

How others can help me: How I can help myself:

_____   _____

_____   _____

_____   _____

_____   _____

A tiny problem: _____

_____

_____

How others can help me: How I can help myself:

_____   _____

_____   _____

_____   _____

_____   _____

I wondered if anyone at the new school would like me. It was my first day there and my stomach was in knots. Then, the teacher said, "Quiet everyone! We have a new student in our class." I was called to the front of the room to introduce myself! Really??? I...

_____

_____

_____

_____

_____

_____

_____

_____

_____

_____

_____

_____

_____

The Best

The best things about my looks are...

_____

_____

_____

_____

_____

_____

_____

Is beauty all about your body—or is it really about
your heart, your mind, your spirit, and more?

_____

_____

_____

_____

_____

_____

_____

The Worst

The worst things about how I look are maybe...

_____

_____

_____

Your worth is not tied to your physical appearance. _100_
Whose standards of good looks or beauty are you
using? Is it fair to compare yourself to celebrities or
stars on social media?

_____

_____

_____

How much time do you spend worrying about your
looks instead of doing things that make you happy?

_____

_____

_____

Failures & Mistakes

Write about your biggest failures or mistakes...

_____

_____

_____

_____

_____

Failure can be your best teacher. Successful people
will tell you that with each failure—comes the seed of
an equal or greater benefit. What are some ways you
can water that seed and grow from your mistakes?

_____

_____

_____

_____

_____

_____

_____

_____

Accomplishments

Talk about your greatest accomplishments...

_____

_____

_____

_____

_____

_____

You've done all these—why not more? Write down some things you hope to achieve in the future:

_____

_____

_____

Now try this—close your eyes and visualize yourself accomplishing one of those goals. Imagine how you would feel in the moment and try to _really feel_ those emotions as if they were real. Picturing yourself as victorious is a powerful way to wire your brain for success. Practice daily and believe you can achieve! When it comes to a goal, whether you think you can or whether you think you can't—you're right!

Kennedy was holding hands with Noah. Everyone could see them. They liked each other and were not afraid to show it. I dreamed about holding hands with someone, too...

_____

_____

_____

_____

_____

_____

_____

_____

_____

_____

_____

_____

_____

_____

If I Could Give...

If I could give away one million dollars any way that I wanted—in any way at all—I would choose to...

_____

_____

_____

_____

_____

_____

_____

_____

_____

_____

_____

_____

_____

_____

_____

_____

_____

But I Can't!

But I can't give away a million dollars. I can do other things that would be nice and help people out, like...

_____

_____

_____

_____

_____

How does helping other people change the way we feel? Could generosity and kindness toward others be a key to our own happiness and well-being?

_____

_____

_____

_____

_____

_____

We went on a fieldtrip to Salamander Park to look at nature. We saw flowers, green moss, and a babbling brook. And of course, salamanders! One of the troublemaker kids was picking the flowers and stepping on the moss. Then they picked up a salamander by the tail and threw it! But the teachers didn't see. I...

_____

_____

_____

_____

_____

_____

_____

_____

_____

_____

_____

_____

_____

The Best Day

The best day of my life was when...

_____

_____

_____

_____

_____

_____

_____

What are all the good emotions and feelings that come back to you when you remember this experience?

_____   _____   _____

_____   _____   _____

_____   _____   _____

_____   _____

Feeling & Emotion Vocabulary Wheel in the back of the book!

_____   _____

Whenever you're feeling down, you can imagine all the feelings from this day to give yourself a mental boost!

The Worst Day

The worst day of my life was maybe...

_____

_____

_____

_____

_____

_____

_____

_____

Negative experiences can add wisdom to a person's
life. What did you learn from this terrible day?

_____

_____

_____

_____

_____

_____

My Five Year

One year from now I'd like...

To be: _____

To have: _____

To let go: _____

To give: _____

Two years from now I'd like...

To be: _____

To have: _____

To let go: _____

To give: _____

Three years from now I'd like...

To be: _____

To have: _____

To let go: _____

To give: _____

Daydream

Four years from now I'd like...

To be: _____

To have: _____

To let go: _____

To give: _____

Five years from now I'd like...

To be: _____

To have: _____

To let go: _____

To give: _____

Decide on some very small things that you can start
doing now to help you grow toward your dreams:

_____

_____

_____

_____

When I found out that we were moving to a new city, I couldn't believe it! I was excited and nervous at the same time. Before my last day in this town, here are all the things that I plan on doing for the very last time...

_____

_____

_____

_____

_____

_____

_____

_____

_____

_____

_____

_____

_____

If I Could Freeze...

If I could freeze time for one day, it would be amazing and totally awesome! I would plan to use my time...

_____

_____

_____

_____

_____

_____

_____

_____

_____

_____

_____

_____

_____

_____

_____

_____

_____

_____

_____

But I Can't!

But I can't freeze time. Time always passes. Here are some good ways and bad ways I spend my time...

Good Uses of Time   *Bad Uses of Time*

_____   _____

_____   _____

_____   _____

_____   _____

_____   _____

_____   _____

_____   _____

If you used your time better, what awesome new things could you make time for in your life?

_____

_____

_____

_____

I got in a fight with my best friend. They called me bad names. And I guess I called them some, too. My feelings were hurt badly. The next time I saw them...

_____

_____

_____

_____

_____

_____

_____

_____

_____

_____

_____

_____

_____

_____

_____

Love & Kindness

The best thing someone did for me was...

_____

_____

_____

_____

_____

_____

_____

Have you done any random acts of kindness for
anyone recently? What's the best thing you think
you've done for someone else?

_____

_____

_____

_____

_____

_____

_____

Hurt & Suffering

The worst thing someone did to me was...

_____

_____

_____

_____

_____

_____

_____

When people hold on to pain and hurt, it turns into suffering. We can't change what happened in the past. Would accepting things as they are help people to let go some of the hurt that they carry around inside?

_____

_____

_____

_____

_____

I was in the kitchen doing homework. My babysitter was making French fries on the stove. They heated hot oil and put the fries in. All of a sudden, the pan caught on fire! My babysitter was screaming! The flames were super high. We didn't know what to do. Then, the babysitter yelled...

_____

_____

_____

_____

_____

_____

_____

_____

_____

_____

_____

_____

If I Could Change...

If I could change one time that I acted out, I would choose the time when...

_____

_____

_____

_____

_____

What led up to this situation? Did anything trigger you?

_____

_____

_____

What were the thoughts in your head at the time?

_____

_____

_____

What emotions or feelings were you experiencing?

_____   _____   _____

_____   _____   _____

_____   _____   _____

Feeling & Emotion Vocabulary Wheel in the back of the book!

But I Can't!

But I can't change how I acted. Here's how I feel now about the choices I made:

_____

_____

_____

_____

How did other people react? How did they feel?

_____

_____

_____

I can think of other ways that I can deal with similar situations in the future. Here's my plan:

_____

_____

_____

_____

_____

I found a note in my desk with my name on it. It was folded in a neat way. I don't know who put it there. I must find out who wrote it! The mysterious note said...

_____

_____

_____

_____

_____

_____

_____

_____

_____

_____

_____

_____

_____

_____

_____

_____

Shame

These are some sad things that make me feel shame...

_____

_____

_____

_____

_____

What would you say to a friend about all these things?
Give yourself the same encouragement or advice that
you would give to a friend or someone that you loved.

_____

_____

_____

_____

_____

_____

_____

_____

Pride

Here are all the great things that make me feel pride...

_____

_____

_____

_____

_____

_____

_____

A healthy amount of pride can help with achievements
and success. Too much pride can hold people back.
How do people act when they have too much?

_____

_____

_____

_____

_____

A Tale of

Avery P.

10 years old

4 ft 7 in 75 lbs.

Sacramento, California

The following is what this suspect reported in a police interview.

Avery reports that an older man lives at the end of his street. Avery and his friends play touch football in the street and sometimes the ball bounces in the neighbors' yard. When the ball goes in the older man's yard on accident, the man always comes out on his porch and yells, "Get off my lawn, you kids!" Avery reports that the older boys in the neighborhood have a "tradition" to wrap the older man's house with toilet paper every year on the night before Halloween. Avery had never taken part in anything like that before. This year his friends planned on carrying on the tradition. Avery said he wanted to be liked by his friends and be a part of the group. The older man was aware of this tradition, too. Every year he had to clean up after the kids. Police had been informed and were ready for the older man to call. When the kids started wrapping his house, the police were notified and arrived to catch the kids in the act. Avery was charged with Criminal Mischief/Nuisance—Toilet Papering a House, a misdemeanor crime, punishable by a fine of up to $1000, up to 3 months in juvenile detention, and 30 hours community service. The case was referred to the youth peer court. As a member of the jury, what do you think the punishment for Avery should be? You can present any punishment to the judge that you think would be suitable for the crime.

True Crime

It was winter. Logan found a small sheet of ice. It looked cool, almost like glass. He picked it up and was joking around. He held it up high and said, "If anyone takes one more step forward—I'll break this over their head!" Emma smiled and took a big step forward, not thinking he would do it. Logan swung the ice down on top of her head and...

_____

_____

_____

_____

_____

_____

_____

_____

_____

_____

_____

_____

If I Could Make...

If I could make one of my problems disappear, my life would be better. I would choose to get rid of...

_____

_____

_____

Here's how my life would be different if this problem were suddenly gone forever:

_____

_____

_____

_____

_____

_____

_____

_____

_____

_____

But I Can't!

But I can't just make a problem disappear. I can brainstorm the pros and cons of doing something versus doing nothing about it, like this:

	Pros	Cons
Doing Something	Pros of trying different things to fix a problem	Cons of trying different things to fix a problem
Doing Nothing	Pros of doing nothing to fix a problem	Cons of doing nothing to fix a problem

Looking at your answers, would it be better to live with the problem or give it your best shot?

_____

_____

My Letter

Write a letter to yourself in the past. Do you have any advice you wish you could tell yourself? What are all the things you want yourself to know about the future? Give yourself the guidance you think past you needs.

_____

_____

_____

_____

_____

_____

_____

_____

_____

_____

_____

_____

_____

_____

_____

_____

_____

to the Past

Mr. MacDonald played a game with his class as a reward. Everyone stood up. The teacher threw a wiffle ball. You caught it and threw it back. If you missed it, you had to sit down. The last kid standing won! Mr. MacDonald threw the ball to Olivia first. Oops! She missed it! She cried and cried and cried in front of the whole class. Then she cried some more! The teacher...

_____

_____

_____

_____

_____

_____

_____

_____

_____

_____

_____

What I Can't Change

These are the things in my life that I can't change...

_____

_____

_____

_____

_____

_____

_____

_____

_____

How much time do you spend worrying about things
that are out of your control? Does it make sense to
worry if there's really nothing you can do?

_____

_____

_____

_____

_____

What I Can Change

Here are the things in my life that I can change...

_____

_____

_____

_____

_____

_____

_____

_____

_____

Many things in your life are a result of your actions.
Sometimes, you and only you have the power to
change a situation—no one is going to do it for you.
Here's how I can change one thing for the better:

_____

_____

_____

_____

Khloe liked riding horses. One day, she was riding her horse and a raccoon came out of the woods. It scared the horse. The horse jumped up on its two back legs! Khloe...

_____

_____

_____

_____

_____

_____

_____

_____

_____

_____

_____

_____

_____

_____

_____

If I Could Mindread...

If I could read other people's minds—like a person with superpowers from the movies, I would totally...

_____

_____

_____

_____

_____

_____

_____

_____

_____

_____

_____

_____

With great power comes great responsibility—how did you choose to use yours? For good or for yourself?

_____

_____

_____

But I Can't!

But I can't read minds. When I want to know what someone is thinking, I can...

_____

_____

_____

_____

How would you rate yourself on being assertive when you talk to someone—you know, being confident and speaking up for yourself, but without being too pushy?

_____

_____

_____

When you want to know what someone is thinking or feeling—or when you think you know and you don't like it—you can keep it inside, or you can be assertive. List some things you can speak up more about:

_____

_____

_____

_____

_____

Self-Care Activities

Go for a walk in nature

Turn off your phone

Write in a journal 😂

Watch the clouds or stars

Meditate

Eat a comfort food

Make a favorite quote list

Stretch or do yoga

Do your nails or a facial

Find positive affirmations

Listen to relaxing music

Do deep breathing

Eat chocolate

Take a cat nap

Create a vision board

Exercise

Take a hot bath or shower

Spend time with a friend

Give hugs

Write a gratitude list

Get a massage

Cuddle with a pet

Distraction List

Watch cute animal videos

Practice a sports move

Do a brain game

Play a video game

Do some doodling

Learn a new dance move

Smell flowers or perfume

Go down a rabbit hole

Work on a hobby

Go through your pictures

Listen to a podcast

Clean a room of the house

Read a book or magazine

Listen to loud music

Count up by 3s, 7s, or 9s

Focus on your five senses

Core Values

Teamwork	Kindness	Respect
Generosity	Courage	Honesty
Family	Humor	Security
Wisdom	Freedom	Fitness
Loyalty	Forgiveness	Creativity
Wealth	Communication	Self-Respect
Gratitude	Power	Fame
Faith	Compassion	Grace
Justice	Excitement	Intelligence
Cooperation	Patience	Friendship
Openness	Advancement	Harmony
Knowledge	Humanity	Love
Success	Diversity	Acceptance
Adventure	Excellence	Spirituality
Beauty	Strength	Leadership
Contentment	Charity	Balance
Wellness	Prosperity	Integrity
Forgiveness	Willingness	Finances
Appreciation	Happiness	Peace

_____   _____   _____

_____   _____   _____

_____   _____   *Add to the list with some of your own!*

Feeling & Emotion

Excited
Pleased
Delighted
Free
Optimistic
Joyful
Cheerful
Blissful
Sickened
Awful
Loathsome
Outraged
Offended
Scorned
Safe
Calm
Thankful
Accepted
Thoughtful
Content
Relaxed
Bored
Busy
Stressed
Dull
Rejected
Embarassed
Disappointed

Happy
Disgust
Peaceful
Bad

Vocabulary wheel

Fear
- Worried
- Insecure
- Scared
- Intimidated
- Alarmed
- Nervous
- Doubtful

Mad
- Aggressive
- Frustrated
- Angry
- Overcritical
- Heated
- Bitter
- Envious

Surprise
- Startled
- Confused
- Amazed
- Shocked
- Stunned

Sad
- Lonely
- Hurt
- Despair
- Depressed
- Guilty
- Vulnerable
- Lost
- Insignificant
- Gloomy

Made in the USA
Monee, IL
06 February 2023

27237169R00090